I've never written a foreword before for anyone, least of all an elflike cartoonist with guileless eyes, an ingratiating smile and a capacity for martinis that is astounding considering his size. Precisely why Hart requested this assignment from me is unknown. I rather think it's because I laugh at his jokes and about one third of the time I'm able to discern some inner and hidden meanings in his wild woolly Left-Bank asides. It happens to be a fact that Johnny Hart is an unusual kind of guy and an unusual kind of humorist. His drawings and his wit can best be described as bold—and boldness is in short supply in the entertainment field nowadays. There are very few practicing humorists, cartoonists or authors who are willing to take an uncharted dip into a strange pool. To Mr. Hart's credit everlasting—he'll swim anywhere, wearing any kind of bathing suit.

To the uninitiated Hart reader, all this will seem pretty meaningless until you read and look at what he's written and drawn. To the Hart fan, this becomes somewhat redundant because you've already become familiar with his imaginative gremlin who makes you look at his pictures twice and reflect on his dialogue at least three times.

It all boils down to this: In the welter of ruttish, threadbare, third-hand humor that we're exposed to day after day, the freshness of Johnny Hart is an air-conditioning unit in a Bedouin tent on the Sahara. It feels good. And that's why I'm writing this foreword—as meaningless as it is—for nothing. So just don't sit there, Johnny Hart, with your leprechaun puss—go ahead and make me laugh!

Rod Serling

B.C.

STRIKES BACK

BY JOHNNY HART

(ABRIDGED)

A FAWCETT GOLD MEDAL BOOK
FAWCETT PUBLICATIONS, INC., GREENWICH, CONN.
MEMBER OF AMERICAN BOOK PUBLISHERS COUNCIL, INC.

Other Fawcett Gold Medal Books by Johnny Hart:

BACK TO B.C. (*abridged*)	D1880
B.C.—BIG WHEEL	D2033
HEY! B.C. (*abridged*)	D2078
HURRAY FOR B.C.	D1904
THE KING IS A FINK (*with Brant Parker*)	D2043
WHAT'S NEW, B.C.?	D1951

50¢ Wherever Paperbacks Are Sold

If your dealer is sold out, send cover price plus 10¢ each for postage and handling to Gold Medal Books, Fawcett Publications, Inc., Greenwich, Conn. 06830. If order is for five or more books, there is no postage or handling charge. Order by number and title. No Canadian orders.

TO A REAL SWEETHEART
OF A BROAD WHO HAS
SOMEHOW WEATHERED IT ALL;
TO MY MATE: BOBBY

I'LL BE GLAD WHEN THEY START MAKING PLASTIC.

THE BASEBALL IS MADE WITH THOUSANDS OF WINDINGS OF STRING.

HOW THE HECK DO YOU WIND STRING INTO A CUBE SHAPE?

SIMPLE.--YOU USE A CUBE FOR THE CORE.

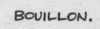

WHAT KIND OF CUBE DID YOU USE?

BOUILLON.

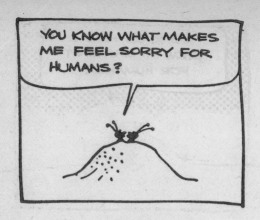

ONLY WILEY COULD SWIM THE DESERT.

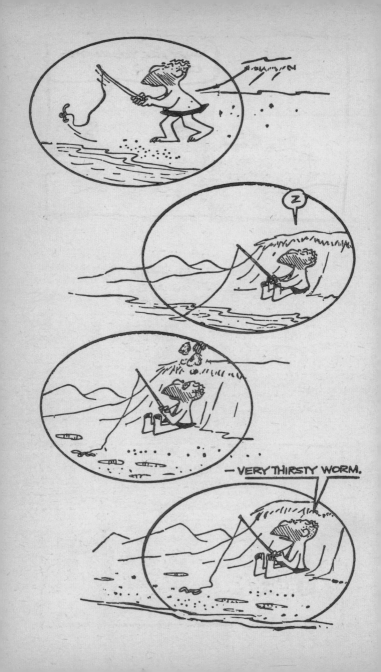

WHOEVER IT IS, DOES A GREAT IMPERSONATION OF WILEY.

POOF

WELCOME TO THE CLUB.

A HEART SHAPED FLOWER.

A GUY NEEDS THAT AT LEAST ONCE A YEAR.

POW

WHAT'S THAT?

I THOUGHT I HEARD SOMETHING! --LIKE HAIR GROWING!

YOU HEAR LOTS OF FUNNY THINGS AT NIGHT.

GOOD HEAVENS.

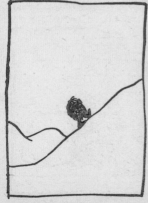

BALD, EH!

THIS IS AN INNOVATION
IN LETTER WRITING:
A "PYRAMID CLUB."
PLEASE MAKE 3
DUPLICATES OF THIS
LETTER AND MAIL THEM
TO ME. —

FORWARD THE ORIGINAL
TO A FRIEND AND ASK HIM TO
DO LIKEWISE. A COMPLETE
EXPLANATION WILL BE FORTH-
COMING, PENDING A SUCCESSFUL
OUTCOME.

THANK YOU,
WILEY.

AFTER A WHILE

HOW DID YOU EVER
MAKE OUT WITH
YOUR 'PYRAMID
CLUB', WILEY?

GREAT.

ZONK

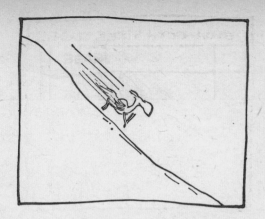

AW, DOGGONE IT!

A GUY CAN'T EVEN RUN DOWN A HILL WITHOUT TAKIN' OFF!

WHAT'S THAT ?
A MAGNIFYING DEVICE.
WHAT DOES IT MAGNIFY ?
EYESTRAIN.

I WONDER HOW COME YOUR FINGERS ONLY BEND DOWN?

DON'T BE SILLY. WHO'D WANT TO HOLD ANYTHING ON THE BACKS OF THEIR HANDS?

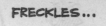

FRECKLES...

I HOPE I CAN MAKE IT TO THE FRECKLE CLINIC.

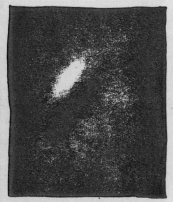